WHERE ARE THEY

LOOK FOR LAURA

ANTHONY TALLARICO

LOOK FOR LAURA
ON THE PLANET
MAXX AND . . .

- ☐ Balloons (3)
- ☐ Birdhouse
- ☐ Birds (2)
- ☐ Books (3)
- ☐ Clipboard
- ☐ Clocks (4)
- ☐ Coffeepot
- ☐ Covered wagon
- ☐ Dog
- ☐ Elephant
- ☐ Evergreen tree
- ☐ Fish
- ☐ Flowerpot
- ☐ Fork
- ☐ Graduate
- ☐ Hamburger
- ☐ Hot dog
- ☐ Ice lolly
- ☐ Kite
- ☐ Old radio
- ☐ Old tyre
- ☐ Pizza
- ☐ Rugby balls (2)
- ☐ Skipping rope
- ☐ Sledge
- ☐ Teepee
- ☐ Train engine
- ☐ Turtle
- ☐ TV set
- ☐ Umbrella

LOOK FOR LAURA IN
THE OCEAN
AND . . .

- ☐ Anchovy
- ☐ Bats (2)
- ☐ Bell
- ☐ Books (2)
- ☐ Bow
- ☐ Cheese
- ☐ Crown
- ☐ Cup
- ☐ Fire hydrant
- ☐ Flowers (2)
- ☐ Ghost
- ☐ Guitar
- ☐ Hammer
- ☐ Haystack
- ☐ Heart
- ☐ Horseshoe
- ☐ Ice-cream cone
- ☐ Key
- ☐ Mermaid
- ☐ Needlefish
- ☐ Octopus
- ☐ Old tyre
- ☐ Pencil
- ☐ Pizza
- ☐ Saw
- ☐ Seesaw
- ☐ Snail
- ☐ Straw hat
- ☐ Telescope
- ☐ Treasure chest
- ☐ Turtles (3)
- ☐ TV set
- ☐ Umbrella

LOOK FOR LAURA
AT THE WATERING
HOLE AND . . .

- ☐ Arrow
- ☐ Ballons (3)
- ☐ Beach ball
- ☐ Birdbath
- ☐ Bird's nest
- ☐ Boat
- ☐ Bones
- ☐ Camel
- ☐ Camera
- ☐ Crocodile
- ☐ Donkey
- ☐ Feather
- ☐ Giraffe
- ☐ Heart
- ☐ Lion
- ☐ Lollipop
- ☐ Owl
- ☐ Pelican
- ☐ Periscope
- ☐ Pig
- ☐ Pumpkin lantern
- ☐ Rooster
- ☐ Rugby ball
- ☐ Snake
- ☐ Socks
- ☐ Tarzan
- ☐ Tin can
- ☐ Toucan
- ☐ Unicorn
- ☐ Wart hog
- ☐ Wolf
- ☐ Worm
- ☐ Yo-yo

LOOK FOR LAURA
ON A SKI SLOPE IN
THE ALPS AND . . .

- [ ] Alligator
- [ ] American football player
- [ ] Artist
- [ ] Boat
- [ ] Bone
- [ ] Bunny
- [ ] Camel
- [ ] Car
- [ ] Cold telephone
- [ ] Dog
- [ ] Elf
- [ ] Evergreen tree
- [ ] Fish
- [ ] Hammock
- [ ] Igloo
- [ ] Kite
- [ ] Mouse
- [ ] Postbox
- [ ] Pumpkin lantern
- [ ] Rake
- [ ] Santa Claus
- [ ] Scuba diver
- [ ] Skateboard
- [ ] Sleeping monster
- [ ] Snowman
- [ ] Sunglasses
- [ ] Top hat
- [ ] Turtle
- [ ] TV aerial
- [ ] Uphill skier

LOOK FOR LAURA
AT THE BAH-HA
BAZAAR AND . . .

- ☐ Beach ball
- ☐ Bird
- ☐ Broom
- ☐ Cat
- ☐ Clouds (2)
- ☐ Coconuts (4)
- ☐ Dog
- ☐ Donkey
- ☐ Elephant
- ☐ Flying carpets (2)
- ☐ Genie
- ☐ Horn
- ☐ Ice-cream cone
- ☐ Igloo
- ☐ Kite
- ☐ Necklace
- ☐ Oil well
- ☐ Pillow fight
- ☐ Rabbit
- ☐ Rugby ball
- ☐ Shovel
- ☐ Skier
- ☐ Sledge
- ☐ Snail
- ☐ Snakes
- ☐ Straw baskets (2)
- ☐ Sunglasses
- ☐ Telescope
- ☐ Tents (4)
- ☐ Truck
- ☐ Turtle
- ☐ Umbrella

LOOK FOR LAURA IN
EUROPE AND . . .

- ☐ Ball
- ☐ Ballerinas (2)
- ☐ Boats (3)
- ☐ Cancan dancers
- ☐ Cars (2)
- ☐ Castle
- ☐ Dog
- ☐ Donkey
- ☐ Egret
- ☐ Fisherman
- ☐ Flying fish
- ☐ Ghost
- ☐ Gondola
- ☐ Hot-air balloon
- ☐ King
- ☐ Knight in armour
- ☐ Non-flying fish (3)
- ☐ Periscope
- ☐ Reindeer
- ☐ Skier
- ☐ Snake
- ☐ Snowmen (2)
- ☐ Starfish
- ☐ Stork
- ☐ Telescope
- ☐ Tour bus
- ☐ Train
- ☐ Tulips
- ☐ Turtle
- ☐ Windmill

LOOK FOR LAURA
AT THE CIRCUS
AND . . .

- ☐ Bad juggler
- ☐ Banana peel
- ☐ Binoculars
- ☐ Bowling ball
- ☐ Bow tie
- ☐ Cactus
- ☐ Cheese
- ☐ Cowboy hats (2)
- ☐ Dry paint
- ☐ Elephants (2)
- ☐ Ghost
- ☐ Hot dog
- ☐ Ice-cream cone
- ☐ Knight in armour
- ☐ Lion
- ☐ Lost shoe
- ☐ Monkey suit
- ☐ Mouse
- ☐ Picture frame
- ☐ Pie
- ☐ Pig
- ☐ Pirate
- ☐ Shoeshine box
- ☐ Skateboards (3)
- ☐ Top hat
- ☐ Training wheels
- ☐ Umbrella
- ☐ Walking flower
- ☐ Watering can

LOOK FOR LAURA AT
SCHOOL AND . . .

- [ ] Alexander
- [ ] Bat
- [ ] Bells (2)
- [ ] Broom
- [ ] Bubble gum
- [ ] Cake
- [ ] Cat
- [ ] Clothes peg
- [ ] Drummer
- [ ] Easel
- [ ] Fish (2)
- [ ] Football
- [ ] Globe
- [ ] Golf club
- [ ] Half moon
- [ ] Happy face
- [ ] Hats (2)
- [ ] Heart
- [ ] Hourglass
- [ ] Igloo
- [ ] Monster mask
- [ ] Owl
- [ ] Paintbrush
- [ ] Pinocchio
- [ ] Plate
- [ ] Protoceratops
- [ ] Robin
- [ ] Robot
- [ ] Rugby ball
- [ ] School bags (2)
- [ ] Scissors
- [ ] Skipping rope
- [ ] Snow
- [ ] Soccer ball
- [ ] Stocking
- [ ] Sunglasses
- [ ] Wastepaper basket

LOOK FOR LAURA
AT THE
WELCOME HOME
PARTY AND . . .

☐ Alien-in-the-box
☐ Baseball cap
☐ Basket
☐ Bone
☐ Cake
☐ Candle
☐ Carrot
☐ Cheese
☐ Evergreen tree
☐ Falling stars (7)
☐ Fire hydrant
☐ Graduate
☐ Guitar
☐ Hamburger
☐ Hammer
☐ Hot dog
☐ Ice-cream soda
☐ Light bulb
☐ Meatball
☐ Mouse
☐ Pencils (2)
☐ Rose
☐ Rugby ball
☐ Screwdriver
☐ Snail
☐ Spade
☐ Tent
☐ Turtle
☐ TV set
☐ Unicorn
☐ Yo-yo

DETECT DONALD   FIND FRANKIE   SEARCH FOR SUSIE   LOOK FOR LAURA